Other books by Exley:
Garden Lovers Quotations
An Illustrated Gardener's Notebook
The Garden Lovers Book of Days
The Crazy World of Gardening
Flowers a Celebration
Roses a Celebration

Published simultaneously in 1994 by Exley
Publications in Great Britain, and Exley Giftbooks in
the USA.

Pictures selected by Helen Exley.
Designed by The Pinpoint Design Company.
Picture research by P. A. Goldberg and J. Clift/Image
Select, London.
Typesetting by Delta, Watford, UK.
Printed and bound in Hungary.

**Exley Publication Ltd, 16 Chalk Hill, Watford, Herts
WD1 4BN, UK.
Exley Giftbooks, 232 Madison Avenue, Suite 1206,
New York, NY 10016, USA.**

Cover: HOSCHEDE'S GARDEN IN MONTGERON
CLAUDE MONET (1840-1926)
Ermitage Museum, St. Petersburg
Scala

Title page: HOLLYHOCKS
HELEN ALLINGHAM (1848-1926)
Bonhams, London
The Bridgeman Art Library, London

• *The Beauty of the* •
GARDEN
A D D R E S S   B O O K

EXLEY
NEW YORK • WATFORD, UK

A

He who plants a garden, plants happiness.
CHINESE PROVERB

A

SUMMER GARDEN
BEATRICE PARSONS (1870-1955)
Christopher Wood Gallery, London
Bridgeman Art Library

B

To own a bit of ground, to scratch it with a hoe, to plant seeds, and watch their renewal of life - this is ... the most satisfactory thing a person can do.
CHARLES DUDLEY WARNER (1829-1900)

B

HILLSIDE OF THE HERMITAGE, PONTOISE
Camille Pissarro (1831-1903)
Musée d'Orsay, Paris
Bridgeman Art Library

B

There is life in the ground: It goes into the seeds, and it also, when it is stirred up, goes into the man who stirs it.
CHARLES DUDLEY WARNER (1829-1900)

C

THE GARDEN, SUTTON PLACE, SURREY
ERNEST SPENCE
Anthony Mitchell Paintings, Northampton
Fine Art Photographic Library

C

Even if I knew certainly the world would end tomorrow, I would plant an apple tree today.
MARTIN LUTHER (1483-1546)

C

IN THE ORCHARD
WALTER BOODLE
Haynes Fine Art, Broadway
Fine Art Photographic Library

D

A Garden is the purest of human pleasures. It is
the greatest refreshment to the spirits of man,
without which ... palaces are but gross handiworks.
FRANCIS BACON, B.1909

D

AT BINSEY, NEAR OXFORD
GEORGE PRICE BOYCE (1826-1897)
Cecil Higgins Art Gallery, Bedford
Bridgeman Art Library

E

I am really as fond of my garden as a young author of his first play.
LADY MARY WORTLEY MONTAGU (1690-1762)

E

F

There is more pleasure in making a garden than in contemplating a paradise.
ANNE SCOTT-JAMES

F

SPRINGTIME FESTIVAL, 1910
WILLIAM LEROY METCALF
Private collection
Art Resource, New York

G

_____

_____

_____

_____

_____

_____

*I have seen him out there among his flowers,
petting them, talking to them, coaxing them till
they simply had to grow.*
J.M. BARRIE (1860-1937)

G

THE HERBACEOUS BORDER
ALFRED DE BREANSKI (1852-1928)
Christopher Wood Gallery, London
Bridgeman Art Library

H

The work rinses out the cup of your spirit, leaves
it washed and clean and ready to be freshly
filled with new hope.
RACHEL PEDEN

H

CHRYSANTHEMUMS
DENIS MILLER BUNKER
GREG HEINS, PHOTOGRAPHER 1983
Isabella Stewart Gardner Museum, Boston
Art Resource, New York

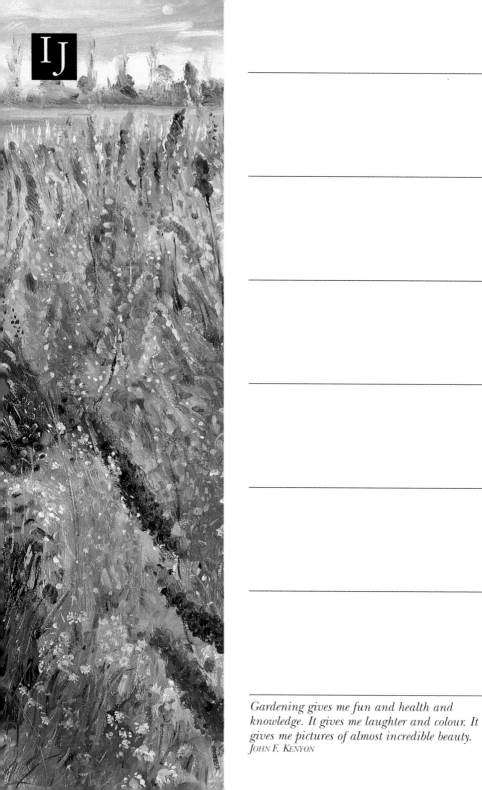

I J

Gardening gives me fun and health and knowledge. It gives me laughter and colour. It gives me pictures of almost incredible beauty.
JOHN F. KENYON

J

DELPHINIUMS AND EMERGING SUN
TIMOTHY EASTON
Private collection
Bridgeman Art Library

J

A Gard'ner's Work is never at an end; it begins with the Year, and continues to the next.
JOHN EVELYN (1620-1706)

K

GARDEN AT ERAGNY
CAMILLE PISSARRO (1831-1903)
Private collection
Edimedia, Paris

L

Though the city may close about him, and the grime and soot descend upon [a gardener], he can still wander in his garden, does he but close his eyes.
BEVERLEY NICHOLS (1898-1983)

HARMONIE ROSE
CLAUDE MONET (1840-1926)
Musée d'Orsay, Paris
AKG-Berlin

M

*It is good to be alone in a garden at dawn or dark
so that all its shy presences may haunt you and
possess you in a reverie of suspended thought.*
JAMES DOUGLAS

M

THE POPPY GARDEN
MAURICE BOMPARD (1857-1936)
Josef Mensing Gallery, Hamm-Rhynern
Bridgeman Art Library

M

Lastly, love your flowers. By some subtle sense the
dear things always detect their friends, and for
them they will live longer and bloom more freely....
JULIA S. BERRALL

FLOWER GARDEN
CLAUDE MONET (1840-1926)
Musée d'Orsay, Paris
Giraudon/Bridgeman Art Library

N

_____

_____

_____

_____

_____

_____

Yes, in the poor man's garden grow
Far more than herbs and flowers -
Kind thoughts, contentment, peace of mind....
MARY HOWITT

CABBAGES IN A COTTAGE GARDEN
CLAUDE STRACHAN (1865-1929)
Fine-Lines (fine art), Warwickshire
Bridgeman Art Library

O

_____

_____

_____

_____

_____

_____

Even if something is left undone, everyone must take time to sit still and watch the leaves turn.
ELIZABETH LAWRENCE

THE POET'S GARDEN
VINCENT VAN GOGH (1853-1890)
Chicago Art Institute
AKG-Berlin

P

_A gardener is never shut out from his garden,
wherever he may be. Its comfort never fails._
BEVERLEY NICHOLS (1898-1983)

P

WATERLILIES: MORNING
CLAUDE MONET (1840-1926)
Musée de l'Orangerie, Paris
Lauros-Giraudon/Bridgeman Art Library

P

_It is utterly forbidden to be half-hearted about
gardening. You have got to love your garden
whether you like it or not._
W.C. SELLAR & R.J. YEATMAN

_____

_____

_____

_____

_____

_____

A COTTAGE GARDEN IN SPRINGTIME
JOHN M. TYSON (FL. 1898-1900)
Bonhams, London
Bridgeman Art Library

R

A garden is like those pernicious machineries which catch a man's coat-skirt or his hand, and draw in ... his whole body to irresistible destruction.
RALPH WALDO EMERSON (1803-1882)

R

THE GREENHOUSE
JOHN FALCONAR SLATER (1857-1937)
Chris Beetles Ltd.
Bridgeman Art Library

R

What was Paradise? but a Garden, an Orchard of Trees and Herbs, full of pleasure, and nothing there but delights....
WILLIAM LAWSON

S

THE VEGETABLE GARDEN WITH TREES IN BLOSSOM,
PONTOISE
CAMILLE PISSARRO (1831-1903)
Musée d'Orsay, Paris
Giraudon/Bridgeman Art Library

But a little garden, the littler the better, is your
richest chance for happiness and success.
REGINALD FARRER

S

HOLLYHOCKS
DAVID WOODLOCK (1842-1929)
Waterman Fine Art Ltd., London
Bridgeman Art Library

S

For a person whose work throws up an agreed
set of figures at the end of each day, a garden is
the last sane place on earth.
PAM BROWN, B.1928

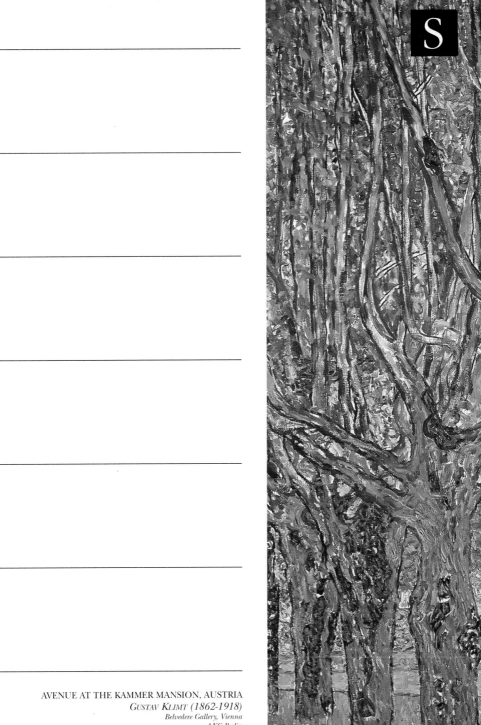

S

AVENUE AT THE KAMMER MANSION, AUSTRIA
GUSTAV KLIMT (1862-1918)
Belvedere Gallery, Vienna
AKG-Berlin

T

April in New England is like first love.
GLADYS TABER

T

APPLE TREES IN BLOSSOM
LOUIS VAN ENGELEN (1856-1940)
By courtesy of Galerie Berko
Fine Art Photographic Library

T

To dig one's own spade into one's own earth!
Has life anything better to offer than this?
BEVERLEY NICHOLS (1898-1983)

MEMORIES OF THE GARDEN AT ETTEN
VINCENT VAN GOGH (1853-1890)
Ermitage, Leningrad
AKG-Berlin

U

In gardening, one's staunchest ally is ...
that strong current which surges through
everything that grows.
JEAN HERSEY

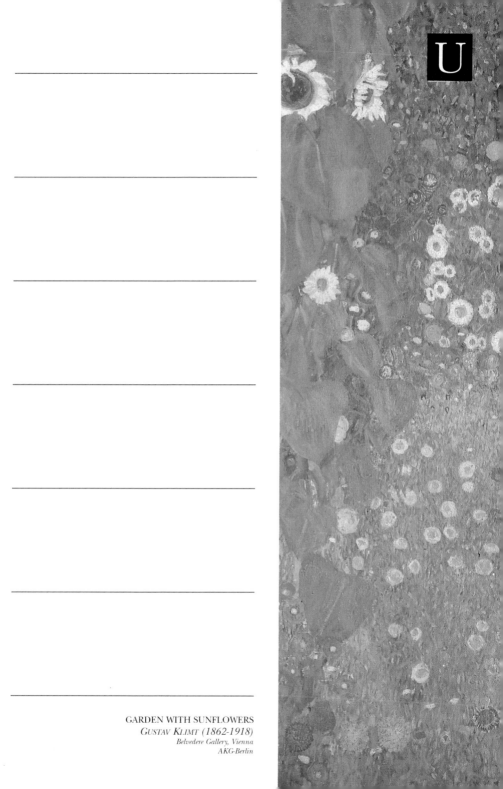

U

GARDEN WITH SUNFLOWERS
GUSTAV KLIMT (1862-1918)
Belvedere Gallery, Vienna
AKG-Berlin

V

I know nothing so pleasant as to sit there on a summer afternoon, with the western sun flickering through the great elder-tree....
MARY MITFORD (1787-1855)

V

HOSCHEDE'S GARDEN
ALFRED SISLEY (1839-1899)
Pushkin Museum, Moscow
AKG-Berlin

A morning-glory at my window satisfies me more than the metaphysics of books.
WALT WHITMAN (1819-1892)

COTTAGE LILIES
EDWARD WILKINS WAITE (1854-1924)
Private collection
Bridgeman Art Library

W

All my hurts
My garden spade can heal.
RALPH WALDO EMERSON (1803-1882)

X Y Z

THE GARDEN
LUCIEN FRANK (1857-1920)
By courtesy of Galerie Berko
Fine Art Photographic Library